Bears In Space

A Book to Read and Color

Written and Illustrated by
Jill E. Osborne

Watermill Press

One evening, four bears relax after supper.

It is a very clear night. They look up into the sky.

The bears see a large white face smiling down at them.

"What can it be?" asks Billy Bear.

"It looks like a big white plate," says Suzy.

7

"I think it looks like a big white balloon,"
Charley exclaims.

"It's Uncle Patrick! Uncle Patrick the Polar Bear!"
Tiny Bear says, jumping up and down. "I see his face."

"Let's take a ride and see," says Billy.

The four bears take off in their spaceship.

The Earth gets smaller and smaller behind them.

They move toward the big white face.

The face gets larger and larger.

"It doesn't look like a face anymore," Suzy says. "What can it be?"

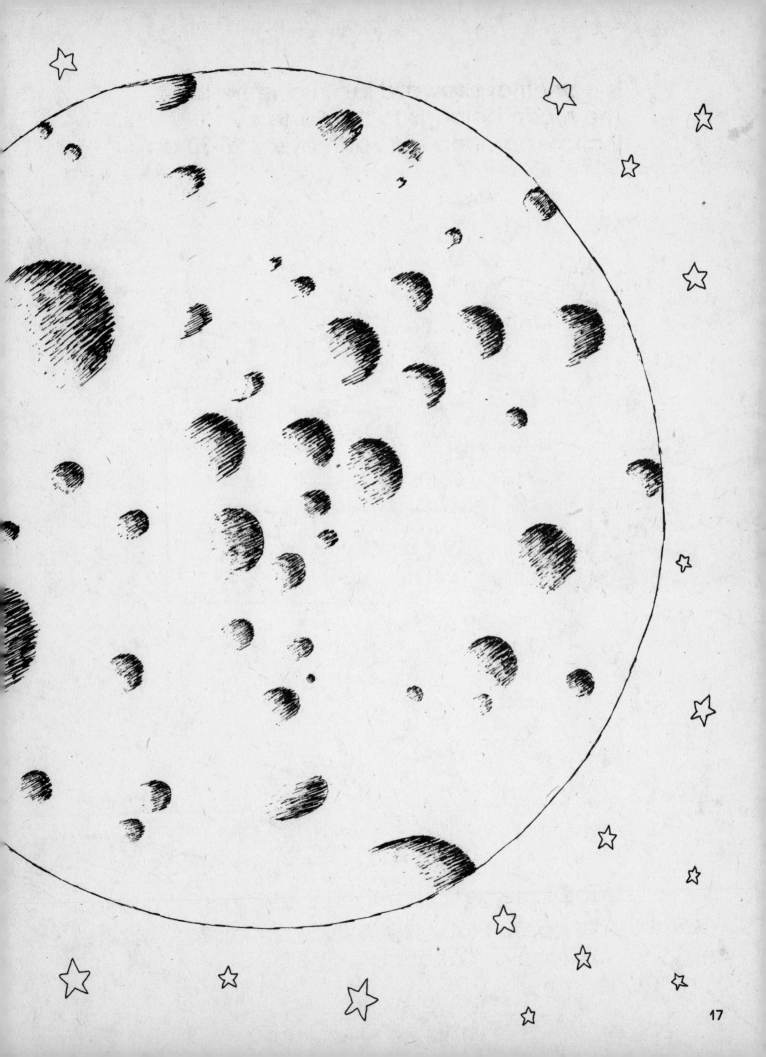

17

Is it another planet? No, it is the moon!
The moon belongs to the Earth.
It circles around the Earth every 28-30 days.

Billy, Suzy, Charley and Tiny Bear land on the moon.

The moon does not have any air for the bears to breathe. They must keep their helmets on. They carry their own air in their helmets.

Charley tries to walk. Instead, he hops.
The moon has little gravity, and so Charley
can hop easily.

Tiny Bear speaks through his helmet radio.
"This is fun! Let's call this the Teddy Bear Hop!"

The bears hop and hop...over hills and down hills...

...into craters and out of craters.

"I am tired of hopping. Let's go home," says Billy.

The four bears take off for Earth.

The moon gets smaller and smaller behind them.

Tiny Bear moves to the back of the spaceship to get a better look.

"The craters are so dark at the bottom of the moon. They look like a face...the face of a bear!" he exclaims.

Suzy says, "We know now that a crater is just a large wide hole in the ground."

The four bears land on Earth. They are glad to be home.

Now, whenever you look into the sky at night
and you see a face, a plate, or a balloon . . .
remember, it's not even Uncle Patrick the Polar Bear—

It's the moon!

The End!